In the
Jaguar's House

Animal Poems & Pictures for Kids

Debbie Hall

Poems & Photos by Debbie Hall
Editing & Book Design by Shawn Aveningo Sanders
Cover Design by Robert R. Sanders

ISBN: 978-1-948461-98-6
Library of Congress Control Number: 2021921430
Printed in the United States of America.
Wholesale Distribution by Ingram.

Published by The Poetry Box®, 2022
   under The Poetry Box for Kids imprint
Portland, Oregon
https://ThePoetryBox.com
530.409.0721

For all the Earth's wild animals
and the people who care for them

"Poetry is a party everyone is invited to."

—Jacqueline Woodson

"Make the Earth your companion.
Walk lightly on it, as other creatures do."

—J. Patrick Lewis

Jaguar

In the Jaguar's House

We have entered
the jaguar's house.

His house has a ceiling
made of sky,

floors of earth, corridors
of rivers and streams.

We enter his world
        (quietly)

so not to disrupt
his daily business.

He watches us
watching him

then plunges back
into pale green water

to catch a plump Capybara
for his midday meal.

Toco Toucan & Picazuro Pigeon

Toucan and Dove

(After Marilyn Nelson's Ostrich and Lark)

Toucan and Dove met each morning
on the same branch
of the same tree.

This pleased the visitors
who came to take their pictures.

Toucan was a bit flashy
with the bright light of her immense beak
and other bold colors.
She enjoyed looking the photographers
straight in the eye.

Dove was feathered
in soft grays and browns,
his beak tiny compared to Toucan's.
He looked away shyly
from all the visitors.

Bedazzled by the amazing Toucan,
people often missed
the quiet message Dove sent them
until they went home
and looked at their pictures.

They almost missed
the shape of his folded wings,
his generous heart.

Laughing Otter

I laugh
         You laugh
We laugh

Guffaw
         Howl
Chortle
         Snicker
Shriek
         Giggle
Whoop
         Snort

Until water
    shoots out
         of our noses

Giant River Otter

Mottled Owl

Night Seer

Her deep dark
saucer eyes
scan the world
around her,
open up the night
with her superb
vision.

When she sees
the brush below
shudder with small life
she swoops
                    D
                        O
                            W
                                N
on silent wings,
ready to snatch her prey
in sharp talons—

Run lizards, run!

Who Goes There?

Child, are you friend or foe?
I need to know.
I've come out from under
my leafy canopy
to better see you.

A gorgeous cat like me
can't be too careful.
Some people want to take
my very fine fur
to make into a coat.

Others might want
to capture me
and sell me as a pet.
If this happened,
my happiness would die.

You understand, don't you?
Yes, you are a friend
and will not harm me.
I'll go back now, into the night
and remember you fondly.

Ocelot

Three-Toed Sloth

Slow-Mo

I'm the slowest
mammal on the planet

no rush no worry
for leisurely me

high up in the treetops
drowsy & dreamy

hanging upside down
for as long as I please

I grow a fine green coat
to match my canopy of leaves

Tufted Coquette

Haiku
for a Hummingbird

What colors you wear
now that you have flirted
with a passing rainbow!

White-Necked Jacobin

Fungus Farmers

Leafcutter ants
fly green sails

of leaves
on their backs,

climb up
long stems

march down
stone paths

stash sails
in nests

underground,
watch the fungi

grow to nourish
their young

who become
the next hardworking,

ever-marching crew
of fungus farmers.

Leafcutter Ants

Capuchin Monkey

Dear Capuchin Monkeys

Thank you for bearing with us humans.
The organ grinders thank you, little performers.
Moviemakers thank you, little actors.
Greyhound racers thank you, little jockeys.
Scientists thank you for your service.
Your human companions thank you for your love.
But now the rainforests and your families need you.
Return to the wild now, Capuchin monkeys,
and nestle safely in the arms of your favorite trees.

Love,

One Who Admires You

Iguana

I have seen
an immense lizard
high in a canopy
of trees,
marveled
at its crest
of dragon-like spines,
craggy head,
its droopy dewlap—
      a chin flap
      that might
      be saying *hello*
      or *stay away*
      this is mine—
its pebbled
and studded skin.
I will call
this creature
a wonderment,
this most splendid
lizard named
iguana.

Green Iguana

Hyacinth Macaws

A Raucous Caucus of Macaws

They swoop down
onto a tree outside our window
and shout:
        WAKE UP! WAKE UP!

Blindingly beautiful brilliant
and blue,
they screech:
        WE'RE HERE! WE'RE HERE!

They flutter their feathers,
flitter about,
chatter and squawk:
        WHO ARE YOU? WHO ARE YOU?

Fabulously friendly,
fun to a fault,
they woo us and whistle:
        LET'S BE FRIENDS! LET'S BE FRIENDS!

Scarlet Ibis

Haiku
for Brilliant Birds

Each day at sunset

they decorate the blue sky—

blazing red arrows

Dear Sea Lion

Are you dreaming,
wrapped up
in your warm coat
of sand,
eyes shut tight?
I too like to roll
on the heated beach
when I emerge
from the sea,
settle under the sun
and dream
of what I will find
next time
I plunge
under the ocean's
glassy surface,
swim through
undulating kelp
looking
for a sea turtle
to guide me
into the depths
of my imagination.

Galapagos Sea Lion

Who's That Following Me?

A strange-looking bird is following me.
　　He's flat and gray and a little see-through.
He flaps his wings whenever I do.
　　What type of bird could this be?
At night he disappears into the dark.
　　When sunlight arrives, so does he!

He looks a bit thin, my odd-looking friend.
　　Perhaps I should feed him some fish.
I guess I don't mind him following me.
　　But could you please help me with this:
What type of bird could this be??

African Penguin

African Elephants

Mighty Me

I come from a mighty herd.
When we walk across the land,
you'll hear a mighty sound,
the trumpeting of magnificent
elephants on the move, mighty
feet kicking up clouds of dirt,
mighty trunks swaying, mighty
ears waving. I am little now,
but already growing mightily—
mighty, mighty me!

Western Lowland Gorillas

About Our Human Relatives

Young one, I know the human animals over there
look a bit strange. They have so little fur on their bodies.

Some of them wear colors as loud as a peacock.
It is hard to believe we are related to these creatures.

There are visitors who watch us with kindness
in their eyes. But some are impolite, pointing,

yelling at us and making strange faces.
They are likely the less intelligent of their species.

Zebras!

They are a riot of stripes
        and oodles of fun!
When you see them together
        you'll never know
where one has ended
        and the other begun!

Burchell's Zebras

African Lion

It's Not Easy Being King

Panthera leo is my fancy name
but you know me as L-I-O-N,
"King of Beasts,"
or "King of the Jungle,"
though I do not live in a jungle
and I'm not always sure
I want to be king.

Oh yes, I stand proud
and have a glorious mane.
My roar is LOUD,
fierce and commanding.
I am the envy of many.
Small prey scurry away
whenever they see me.

But sometimes, I'd like to be
a monkey swinging high
in a tree, a sweet nightingale
or a zebra prancing
its dizzying stripes.
A lion can dream, can't he?
After all, it's not always
easy being king.

Advice for a Young Rhinoceros

Rhino, what a fine long

Horn you are growing! But run now

Into the bush! You

Never know who might want to

Own your precious body.

Southern White Rhinoceros

Warthog

Ode to a Warthog

O delightful little piggy
with your tiny curvy tusks
and itty-bitty beady eyes,
you're worth a thousand likes.

Your humungous head
holds loads of smarts.
You're tough and sturdy,
bristly and bold.

You are fleet of foot
in your high-heeled hooves.
O well-mannered beastie,
you even curtsy when you eat!

Dung Beetle

Rollin', Rollin', Rollin'

Rolling
his heavy ball
of elephant poo
up the earthen hill
Dung beetle makes haste
under hot sun and navigates by the
Milky Way through the inky night.
Dung beetles feed, breed and shelter
in rich droppings of other animals.
You might say one animal's waste
is another's treasure. You might
say Dung beetles are the
ultimate recyclers.

Mr. Gnu (G-new) to You

I'm not your average-looking antelope.
Some say I am not properly built.
    I say, *by whose standards?*

My front end is heavy, my hindquarters slight.
My head is shaped like a rectangle.
    I call this *interesting*.

I carry this heavy body on spindly legs.
Some refer to me as ungainly.
    I say, *watch me thunder across the plains.*

I'm not your average-looking antelope.
You need not call me handsome.
    But you may call me *amazing*.

Wildebeest (a.k.a. Gnu)

Rock Hyrax

Ain't No Rules

In the wild,
grab as big a piece
of food
as you can find,

      eat with your mouth open,
      make lots of noise:
            CRUNCH
            SLURP
            BURP
      go back for more—
      ten times if you want—

and no one
never ever
calls you rude.

If I Come Back to Life
as a Different Animal

I'd surely like to be a giraffe,
          so tall I could touch the clouds
                    with my head,

glide like a slow wave
          as I stride across the plains
                    resembling royalty,

gaze at all the smaller creatures
          underneath me
                    with a gentle love.

Masai Giraffe

Tankas for Two Monkeys

1.

Monkey's eyes grow big
Mouth wide open in surprise
What is she watching?
I hope it is a tiger!
If so, she'll run away soon

Langur Monkey

2.

What is lost is lost
The monkey looked all over
Wait—nothing is lost
This monkey admires himself
in a mirror of water

Langur Monkey

Polar Bear

A Bear of Many Names

Ursus maritimus, Thalarctos,
sea bear, ice bear, Nanuq,
isbjorn, white bear, *beliy medved*,
lord of the Arctic,
old man in the fur cloak
or white sea deer.

This bear is built for the cold.
This bear calls the sea ice home,
but his home is shrinking
as the world is warming
                                        too much.

Imagine your house—and all
the other houses around you
shrinking—
so much that only a mouse
could live in your house.

This bear needs you and me
to help save his home.
This bear of many names
never wants to be called
                                        ghost bear.

Red Dragonfly

She comes to the pond
in the heat of summer,

wraps her forelegs
around a plant stem,

and rests over water
bubbling with orange koi.

Her wings are clear
like windows

with dozens of tiny panes.
If you look through them

you may see a kaleidoscope
of colors, the silk thread

of a spider's web
or a feather drifting by.

If you invite her back
in your most sincere voice,

she might gift you
with her return.

Dragonfly

Afterword

First of all, thank you for reading this book. I hope you've enjoyed the poems and photographs of wild animals as much as I enjoyed making them. I have been very fortunate to travel the world to see these wonderful creatures and the lands in which they live. While I have always loved animals, my travels have deepened that love and appreciation for wildlife. This book was created so that I might share this appreciation with others.

Many animals in the world—a number of them featured in this book—are in serious danger. Reasons for this include climate change, habitat loss, the illegal wildlife trade and hunting by humans. Some animals, like the rhinoceros and African lions, are far too close to extinction in the wild. However, we can build a better future for our wildlife together. Kids can make a big difference by becoming superheroes for the earth and *all* of its inhabitants. At the end of this book are resources for you to explore ways you can help.

Fun Facts about These Animals

JAGUARS are the third largest cats in the world, after tigers and lions. The spots on their fur are called "rosettes," because they are shaped like roses. They are at home in trees or on the ground and are strong swimmers. They eat fish, turtles and caimans found in rivers and larger animals such as deer, capybara and tapirs. Jaguars used to be found from the southwestern United States all the way to Argentina, but now they occupy less than half of their previous range, in part due to habitat loss and the illegal wildlife trade.

TOCO TOUCANS live in South America's tropical forests. They are known for their big, colorful bills. Their bill is a very useful feeding tool. They can reach fruit high on branches that are too small to support their weight. The saw-like edges of their bills are great for peeling fruit. Their vocalizations are often compared to the croaking sounds of frogs.

The **PICAZURO PIGEON** is one of well over 300 species of pigeons seen almost everywhere on earth. It is native to South America and lives in a range of habitats—from urban areas to light woodlands.

GIANT RIVER OTTERS are more than twice as long as North American river otters, reaching up to 6 feet in length. They are very social animals and often live in groups of up to 20 individuals. They are expert fishers. In Brazil the giant river otter is known as "ariranha," which means "water jaguar." They have few predators, but the actual jaguar is one of them.

The **MOTTLED OWL** is a common forest owl and can be seen throughout much of Central and South America. It has large eyes, which provide excellent vision for hunting at night. This owl can move its head nearly all the way around without moving its body. Its "gruff hoots" may sound like a dog barking.

OCELOTS have very fine and gorgeous fur, which makes them vulnerable to the illegal fur trade. Fortunately, they are protected in the U.S. and most other countries where they live. Ocelots are about twice the size of a house cat. They are active mostly at night and are quite secretive. Their eyes have a special layer that collects light, so ocelots can see much better in the dark than we can.

SLOTHS are the world's slowest mammal. The **THREE-TOED SLOTH** is so inactive that algae grow on its furry coat. Algae helps give it camouflage in the trees of the rainforest where it lives, letting it blend in with the green leaves. Even though sloths resemble monkeys with their long arms and shaggy fur, they are actually related to armadillos and anteaters.

Some have called **HUMMINGBIRDS** "avian helicopters," because of their ability to stay in one place during flight, fly forward and back, and upside down too. The average weight of a hummingbird is less than a nickel. The **TUFTED COQUETTE** is a tiny hummingbird that often resembles a large bee as it moves from flower to flower, feeding on nectar. The **WHITE-NECKED JACOBIN** is a major pollinator of many flowers and will chase other birds away from where it is feeding. Both of these hummingbirds can be seen in areas ranging from Mexico to Brazil.

LEAFCUTTER ANTS are tiny creatures—about the same size as an eraser on a pencil—that can carry as much as 50 times their weight. Though you might think they eat the leaves they bite off trees, instead they plant them in underground nests. As the plant material decays, fungus grows and it is the fungus that feeds the ants. Think of the leaves as fertilizer used to grow their crops.

CAPUCHIN MONKEYS are intelligent and adaptable animals important to the ecology of the rainforest. In the past, humans have trained Capuchin monkeys to perform in many TV shows and movies and to serve people in other ways. Now we know that this is not best for these animals. They belong in the wild where they live in large groups of 10-35 other monkeys.

The **GREEN IGUANA'S** crest of spines, craggy head and droopy dewlap (a flap of skin under its neck) reminds many people of dinosaurs or dragons. Green iguanas' favored habitat is a canopy of trees, where they like to bask on branches that hang over water. Sometimes iguanas sleep in each other's arms or on top of one another.

HYACINTH MACAWS are the largest parrots (by length) in the world. They are social birds that are quite loud and very smart. They can mimic human speech. Hyacinth macaws are popular birds among pet owners. Trapping of these birds for the pet trade and habitat loss has meant far fewer of them in the wild. Fortunately there are organizations helping to protect them and increase their numbers back in the wild.

To witness thousands of **SCARLET IBIS** return to their roosting places at sunset is a once-in-a-lifetime experience. They are one of the two national birds of Trinidad and Tobago. They live in flocks of 30 or more, being quite sociable and community-minded birds.

GALAPAGOS SEA LIONS are often found sleeping on the beaches or swimming close to shore. They can stay underwater for over 10 minutes at a time and mostly feed on sardines. On land they might look clumsy as they waddle around. However, once in the water they transform into graceful and fast swimmers. They are found in only two places—the Galapagos Islands and a place called Isla de la Plata off the coast of Ecuador.

Some have described **AFRICAN PENGUINS** as "black and white and cute all over." One of the smallest penguin species in the world, they live in a warmer climate than many other penguins. If you look closely at their faces, you will see a pink patch of bare skin over each eye. These patches help keep the penguins cool in hot temperatures. Penguins do not fly, but instead use their wings like flippers in the water. They have a loud call that sounds like a donkey braying.

AFRICAN ELEPHANTS are the largest animals walking the earth, weighing from 2-1/2 to 7 TONS! They are known as a "keystone species," which means they play an important role in their ecosystem. An elephant's trunk has an amazing number of uses. Elephants are better smellers than bloodhounds and can detect water sources from up to 12 miles away. They use their trunks to snorkel through deep water, say "hello" to each other, to drink water, feed on grass and leaves, and to pet each other in times of stress. Elephants are very social and form close family bonds. Certain elephant species are critically endangered, in part due to poaching for their ivory tusks.

WESTERN LOWLAND GORILLAS are truly our close relatives, sharing as much as 98% of their genes with human beings. They are very gentle animals that live in groups called troops. Although gorillas are normally quiet, they have 22 different hoots, barks and screams, each meaning something different. No two gorilla noses are alike, so scientists use photos of gorilla faces to tell who is who. The big toe of a gorilla's foot is "opposable," like our thumbs, which helps it grab food and climb trees.

BURCHELL'S ZEBRAS are members of the horse family. No two zebras' stripe patterns are the same. Because of this, they can be identified just like humans can be told apart by their fingerprints. Zebras use their stripe patterns to recognize each other.

The **AFRICAN LION** is the second largest member of the cat family, but its roar is the loudest. It is so loud it can be heard from five miles away! African lions have been admired throughout history for their courage and strength. Interestingly, the female lions are the ones who do most of the hunting and rule the pride (a group of lions that live together). The male lions guard the pride and protect their territory. African lions are at high risk of extinction in the wild. Key to their survival is helping humans learn how to better live with lions.

RHINOCEROS are mammals just like us, even though they look like prehistoric creatures. They can gallop up to 30 miles per hour. Rhinos once roamed many places throughout Europe, Asia and Africa. Sadly, very few rhinoceros survive outside national parks and preserves. This is due to a demand for their horns by humans. The **SOUTHERN WHITE RHINOCEROS** has benefitted from conservation efforts, but there is much more work to be done on behalf of all rhinos in the wild.

"Beauty is more than skin deep" might be well applied to **WARTHOGS**, who, to many, are funny looking creatures. Warthogs are pigs that live in

Africa. They like to roll in the mud just like other types of pigs. They kneel on their front legs to eat short grasses. When they run, they usually carry their tails straight up and the tuft on top looks like a flag.

DUNG BEETLES are found wherever there is dung, also known as poop. They eat the dung of other animals, which is very nutritious for these beetles. Dung beetles are divided into three groups: rollers, tunnelers and dwellers. The words describe how the beetles use the dung.

WILDEBEESTS (GNUS) are members of the antelope family. Their migration is one of the most breathtaking wildlife events on earth, involving up to 1.5 million wildebeests at a time! You will often see them grazing and migrating with zebras. Wildebeests are always on the move and tend to be rather noisy creatures.

The **ROCK HYRAX** looks a little like a large guinea pig but is actually a relative of the elephant. Two of its large incisor teeth grow out to be tiny tusks just like the elephant's. Its feet are built for rock-climbing. These little animals have many predators, including: leopards, hyenas, jackals, pythons, and eagles. Fortunately, they have excellent vision that allows them to spot danger from over 1,000 yards away!

MASAI GIRAFFE are one of the largest subspecies of giraffe, which are the tallest living animals. A giraffe could look into a second story window without having to stand on its tiptoes. A giraffe's feet are the size of a dinner plate and its six-foot neck weighs 600 pounds! Long ago, the giraffe was called a "camel-leopard," because people thought it was a combination of a camel and a leopard. The Masai giraffe was declared an endangered species in 2019.

In India, **LANGUR MONKEYS** have been trained to scare off wild animals that wander into public spaces. They normally eat plants but accept human food handouts as well. They will also eat spider webs and insect larvae. They are considered sacred in the Hindu religion, so they can roam freely around villages and temples in India.

POLAR BEARS are the largest bears in the world. Their huge paws act like snowshoes when they walk in deep snow. They also use their large front paws like paddles when they swim. Polar bears look white to us, but their fur is actually clear and the skin underneath is black. To clean their fur, these bears roll in the snow. Climate change is their greatest threat, as a warming world melts the sea ice upon which they depend.

DRAGONFLIES are expert fliers. They can fly straight up and down and hover like a helicopter. They also have incredible vision, as nearly all of their head is eye. They help humans by eating lots of mosquitoes. A dragonfly called the "Globe Skimmer" has the longest migration of any insect. It travels 11,000 miles back and forth across the Indian Ocean!

RESOURCES

For information on how kids can help wildlife, visit these websites:

kids.nationalgeographic.com/nature/save-the-earth

sandiegozookids.org/save-animals

www.worldwildlife.org

endextinction.org

For further reading:

Alarcón, Francisco X. *Animal Poems of the Iguazú. Animalario del Iguazú.* Illus. Maya Christina Gonzalez. New York: Children's Book Press (Lee and Low Books): 2008.

Heard, Georgia. *Creatures of Earth, Sea, and Sky.* Illus. Jennifer Owings Dewey. Honesdale, PA: WordSong, 1992.

Lewis, J. Patrick (Ed.). *National Geographic Book of Animal Poetry.* Washington, D.C.: National Geographic, 2012.

Sidman, Joyce. *Song of the Water Boatman & Other Pond Poems.* Illus. Beckie Prange. Boston: Houghton Mifflin Company, 2005.

Sidman, Joyce. *Hello Earth! Poems to Our Planet.* Illus. Miren Asiain Lora. Grand Rapids, MI: Eerdmans Books for Young Readers, 2021.

Tuttle, Sarah Grace. *Hidden City: Poems of Urban Wildlife.* Illus. Amy Schimler-Safford. Grand Rapids, MI: Eerdmans Books for Young Readers, 2018.

Yolen, Jane. *Birds of a Feather.* Photographs by Jason Stemple. Honesdale, PA: WordSong, 2011.

CPSIA information can be obtained
at www.ICGtesting.com
Printed in the USA
BVHW022054220522
637756BV00011B/114